The
Building Resiliency Workbook

Reproducible Self-Assessments, Exercises & Educational Handouts

Ester A. Leutenberg

John J. Liptak, EdD

Illustrated by

Amy L. Brodsky, LISW-S

wholeperson
Stress & Wellness Publishers

wholeperson
Stress & Wellness Publishers

101 W. 2nd St., Suite 203
Duluth MN 55802

800-247-6789

books@wholeperson.com
www.wholeperson.com

The Building Resiliency Workbook
Reproducible Self-Assessments, Exercises & Educational Handouts

Printed in the United States of America

10 9 8 7 6 5 4 3 2

Editorial Director: Carlene Sippola
Art Director: Joy Morgan Dey

Library of Congress Control Number: 2010937662
ISBN: 978-1-57025-247-1

Using This Book *(For the professional)*

Resiliency has been defined as the ability to:

- manage life's challenges, stresses, changes, and pressures effectively.
- cope and adapt successfully to adversity.
- bounce back to a balanced state after facing a major disruption in life or career.

People have an innate ability to demonstrate resiliency when they have resiliency skills built into their lives. Resilient people are able to adapt successfully under adverse circumstances such as: poverty, mental illness, disasters, terrorism, physical or psychological trauma, divorce, job loss, prison, loss of a loved one, parent's divorce, prolonged stress, physical or sexual abuse, or a lack of safety. Resiliency, or a positive behavioral adaptation, is critical when people encounter any type of trauma.

Research shows that resiliency offers protection from distress and illness in the face of change or adversity. The presence of high levels of resiliency is associated with these factors:

- high level of happiness.
- high level of self-esteem.
- high sense of energy and vitality.
- high level of optimism.
- high level of self-reported health.
- high sense of meaning and direction.
- low level of depression.

People who are resilient . . .

- work because they enjoy it.
- react in an optimistic way.
- see problems as challenges.
- take positive action.
- think of change as natural and go with the flow.
- thrive under challenging situations.
- find it easy to be content in various situations.
- believe that they can influence events and their reactions to events.
- recognize that with stress comes growth.

Research also indicates that resiliency can be built. The purpose of this workbook is to provide participants with the requisite skills they need to manage their emotions and to develop and maintain resiliency.

(Continued)

Using This Book *(For the professional, continued)*

The Building Resiliency Workbook contains five separate sections to help participants learn more about themselves and how to build resiliency which will enable them to thrive in times of adversity, change and stress. They will learn about the importance of building resiliency skills to turn change and stress into opportunities and challenge, to live life zestfully, and to take positive actions in order to live their lives with less stress.

The sections of this book:

- **OPTIMISTIC OUTLOOK SCALE** helps participants identify how optimistically they view and live life.

- **LOCUS OF CONTROL SCALE** helps participants explore the extent to which they believe they have control over what happens in their lives.

- **SENSE-OF-SELF SCALE** helps participants explore the strength of their self-esteem, self-confidence and self-concept.

- **ABILITY TO BOUNCE BACK SCALE** helps participants increase their ability to bounce back and recover from a setback.

- **CHANGE MANAGEMENT SCALE** helps participants to become aware of how well they deal with change, and develop skills necessary to accept change.

These sections serve as avenues for individual self-reflection, as well as participating in group experiences revolving around identified topics of importance. Each assessment includes directions for easy administration, scoring and interpretation. Each section includes exploratory activities, reflective journaling activities and educational handouts to help participants discover their level of resiliency and provides reflective exercises and instruction to build personal and professional resiliency.

The art of self-reflection goes back many centuries and is rooted in many of the world's greatest spiritual and philosophical traditions. Socrates, the ancient Greek philosopher, was known to walk the streets engaging the people he met in philosophical reflection and dialogue. He felt that this type of activity was so important in life that he went so far as to proclaim, "The unexamined life is not worth living!" The unexamined life is one in which the same routine is continually repeated without ever thinking about its meaning to one's life and how this life really could be lived. However, a structured reflection and examination of beliefs, assumptions, characteristics, and patterns can provide a better understanding, which can then lead to a more satisfying life. A greater level of self-understanding about important life skills is often necessary to make positive, self-directed changes. The assessments and

(Continued)

Using This Book *(For the professional, continued)*

exercises in this book can help promote this self-understanding. Through involvement in the in-depth activities, the participant claims ownership in the development of positive behavioral patterns.

Journaling is an extremely powerful tool for enhancing self-discovery, learning, transcending traditional problems, breaking ineffective life habits, and helping oneself to heal from psychological traumas of the past. From a physical point of view, writing reduces stress and lowers muscle tension, blood pressure and heart rate levels. Psychologically, writing reduces sadness, depression and general anxiety, and leads to a greater level of life satisfaction and optimism. Behaviorally, writing leads to enhanced social skills, emotional intelligence and creativity. It also leads to improved resiliency and the ability to deal effectively with adversity and stress in life.

By combining reflective assessment and journaling, participants will be exposed to a powerful method of combining verbalizing and writing to reflect on and to solve problems. Participants will become more aware of the strengths and weaknesses of their resiliency and find ways to build and enhance their hardiness.

Preparation for using the assessments and activities in this book is important. The authors suggest that prior to administering any of the assessments in this book, you complete them yourself. This will familiarize you with the format of the assessments, the scoring directions, the interpretation guides and the journaling activities. Although the assessments are designed to be self-administered, scored and interpreted. This familiarity will help facilitators prepare to answer questions about the assessments.

The Assessments, Journaling Activities, and Educational Handouts

The Assessments, Journaling Activities, and Educational Handouts in *The Building Resiliency Workbook* are reproducible and ready to be photocopied for participants' use. Assessments contained in this book focus on self-reported data and are similar to those used by psychologists, counselors, therapists and marriage and family therapists. Accuracy and usefulness of the information provided is dependent on the truthful information that each participant provides through self-examination. By being honest, participants help themselves to learn more about how they respond and react to stress, change, and adversity in their lives, and to uncover information that might be keeping them from being as happy and/or as successful as they might be.

An assessment instrument can provide participants with valuable information about themselves; however, it cannot measure or identify everything about them. The purpose of the assessments is not to pigeon-hole certain characteristics, but rather to allow participants to explore all of their characteristics. This book contains self-assessments, not tests. Tests measure knowledge or whether something is right or wrong. For the assessments in this book, there are no right or wrong answers. These assessments ask for personal opinions or attitudes about a topic of importance in the participant's career and life.

When administering assessments in this workbook, remember that the items are generically written so that they will be applicable to a wide variety of people. They will not account for every possible variable for every person. The assessments are not specifically tailored to one person. Use them to help participants identify possible negative themes in their lives and to find ways to break the hold that these patterns and their effects have.

Advise participants taking the assessments that they should not spend too much time trying to analyze the content of the questions; their initial response will most likely be true. Regardless of individual scores, encourage participants to talk about their findings and their feelings pertaining to what they have discovered about themselves. Resilient people are able to adapt successfully and cope with stress and catastrophe. They have the ability to bounce back to a balanced state after disruption or transition. These resiliency-building exercises can be used by facilitators working with any population who are experiencing disruptions in their lives.

A particular score on any assessment does not guarantee a participant's level of resiliency happiness. Use discretion when using any of the information or feedback provided in this workbook. The use of these assessments should not be substituted for consultation and/or counseling from a psychological or medical professional.

Thanks to the following professionals whose input in this book has been so valuable!

Kathy Khalsa, OTR/L	Eileen Regen, M.Ed., CJE
Jay Leutenberg	Lucy Ritzic, OTR/L
Kathy Liptak, Ed.D.	Eileen Rotman

Layout of the Book

This book includes the following reproducibles in all 5 sections:

- **Assessment Instruments** – Self-assessment inventories with scoring directions and interpretation materials. Group facilitators can choose one or more of the activities relevant to their participants.

- **Activity Handouts** – Practical questions and activities that prompt self-reflection and promote self-understanding. These questions and activities foster introspection and promote pro-social behaviors.

- **Quotations** – Quotations are used in each chapter to provide insight and promote self-reflection and promote self-understanding. Participants will be asked to select one or more of the quotations and journal about what the quotations mean to them.

- **Reflective Questions for Journaling** – Self-exploration activities and journaling exercises specific to each assessment to enhance self-discovery, learning, and healing.

- **Educational Handouts** – Handouts designed to supplement instruction can be used individually or in groups. They can be distributed, converted into masters for overheads or transparencies, scanned for use as a presentation.

Who should use this program?

This book has been designed as a practical tool for helping professional therapists, counselors, marriage and family therapists, psychologists, teachers, group leaders, etc. Depending on the role of the professional using *The Building Resiliency Workbook* and the specific group's needs, these sections can be used individually, combined, or implemented as part of an integrated curriculum for a more comprehensive approach.

Why use self-assessments?

Self-assessments are important in teaching various life skills. Participants will . . .

- Become aware of the primary motivators that guide behavior.

- Explore and learn to indentify potentially harmful situations.

- Explore the effects of messages received in childhood.

- Gain insight that will guide behavioral change.

- Focus thinking on behavioral goals for change.

- Uncover resources that can help to cope with problems and difficulties.

- Explore personal characteristics without judgment.

- Develop full awareness of personal strengths and weaknesses.

Because the assessments are presented in a straightforward and easy-to-use format, individuals can self-administer, score, and interpret each assessment independently.

Introduction for the Participant

Resiliency is the ability to:

- deal effectively with stress and adversity.
- successfully handle changes in life.
- withstand grief and accept loss.
- creatively adapt to life challenges.

Psychologically hardy people tend to have less stress, anxiety and depression. They have more stable family lives and satisfying marriages. They progress further in their careers and live with more contentment.

Everyone has a share of stressors and challenges. You are no different. The most important factor is how you experience stress and face challenges. It is important to discover how you perceive them, how you think these experiences might affect your future, and how effectively you are able to cope. This is the true level of your personal resilience.

Research shows these factors of resiliency:

- Your thinking and your subsequent behavioral habits create either bridges or barriers to a better future. This workbook will help you to explore your thinking and develop positive behavioral habits that will help you to live better now as well as build a better future for yourself.

- Resiliency can be learned. You can use this workbook to help you grow personally and develop critical resiliency characteristics that will allow you to deal effectively with adversity, change, stress and any challenges that life throws at you.

- The struggle to bounce back and recover from setbacks can lead to the development of resources you did not know you had. This workbook will provide you with the opportunity to look at the stress and adversity in your life, explore how you have handled stress and adversity in the past, and learn new ways to more effectively and positively deal with setbacks in your life.

The Building Resiliency Workbook is designed to help you learn more about yourself; identify the stresses and challenges in your life; explore how you have dealt with adversity in the past; develop resiliency skills and a resiliency mindset; and find better ways to use these newfound skills to deal effectively with whatever setbacks you encounter in life. You will be encouraged to complete assessments, journaling activities and exercises. Because active involvement and "doing" is as important as learning theories, it is critical that you take the time to complete all of the skill-building exercises.

The Building Resiliency Workbook
TABLE OF CONTENTS

TABLE OF CONTENTS

TABLE OF CONTENTS

TABLE OF CONTENTS

SECTION I:
Optimistic Outlook Scale

Name_____

Date_____

Optimistic Outlook Scale Directions

Some people see the glass half full, while others see it half empty. The first group of people are called optimists and the second group are called pessimists. As an optimist, regardless of transitions, setbacks, or disappointments, the person looks at the bright side and sees the possibilities life has to offer. Optimists expect good things to happen, expect to be able to solve problems efficiently, and plan to accomplish their life and work goals. They go through life with positive outlooks and are content most of the time.

Optimists maintain a positive world-view. Pessimists think negatively and cynically about the world. The Optimistic Outlook Scale is designed to help you assess your outlook when negative and positive things happen in your life.

This scale contains 40 statements that are divided into four resiliency categories. Read each of the statements and decide whether or not the statement describes you. For each of the statements listed, circle the number of your response on the line to the right of each statement.

In the following example, the circled 4 indicates the statement is very much like the person completing the assessment:

	Very Much Like Me	Usually Like Me	Not Usually Like Me	Not Like Me
1. When things go wrong, I remain hopeful	(4)	3	2	1

This is not a test and there are no right or wrong answers. Do not spend too much time thinking about your answers. Your initial response will be the most true for you. Be sure to respond to every statement.

(Turn to the next page and begin)

Optimistic Outlook Scale

	Very Much Like Me	Usually Like Me	Not Usually Like Me	Not Like Me
1. When things go wrong, I remain hopeful 4	3	2	1
2. A lot of situations do not have a "silver lining" 1	2	3	4
3. I can always see the light at the end of the tunnel. . . . 4	3	2	1
4. I often feel hopeless 1	2	3	4
5. I look on the bright side of things.. 4	3	2	1
6. I'm usually optimistic about my future 4	3	2	1
7. I am unhappy a lot of the time. 1	2	3	4
8. I rarely get depressed when I think about the future. 4	3	2	1
9. I do not wait for happiness to find me. 4	3	2	1
10. I often feel helpless when things change. 1	2	3	4

H - TOTAL = _____

	Very Much Like Me	Usually Like Me	Not Usually Like Me	Not Like Me
11. In uncertain times, I usually expect the best 4	3	2	1
12. If something can go wrong, it will 1	2	3	4
13. I usually expect things to go my way 4	3	2	1
14. Things usually don't work out the way I want them to 1	2	3	4
15. I am afraid to hope that good things will happen to me. 1	2	3	4
16. I often say "good things never happen to me". 1	2	3	4
17. My problems seem to never end.. 1	2	3	4
18. Even if I have failed in the past, I do not expect to fail again. 4	3	2	
19. I usually maintain a positive attitude in life 4	3	2	1
20. I feel like I have no control over what happens in my life 1	2	3	4

L - TOTAL = _____

(Continued on the next page)

(Optimistic Outlook Scale continued)

	Very Much Like Me	Usually Like Me	Not Usually Like Me	Not Like Me
21. I usually talk about positive things	4	3	2	1
22. I often do not look for the good things in people	1	2	3	4
23. I see the "glass as half full" not "half empty"	4	3	2	1
24. I have had a hard time seeing the possibilities of a situation	1	2	3	4
25. Every day holds numerous opportunities..	4	3	2	1
26. When faced with a challenge, my first thought is positive	4	3	2	1
27. I remain positive even when things do not go my way.	4	3	2	1
28. I see every day as a new opportunity at life.	4	3	2	1
29. I often find myself waiting for happiness to find me . . .	1	2	3	4
30. I believe that things will work out the way I want	4	3	2	1

A - TOTAL = _____

	Very Much Like Me	Usually Like Me	Not Usually Like Me	Not Like Me
31. I set specific life goals and work toward them.	4	3	2	1
32. I often lack confidence in myself.	1	2	3	4
33. I believe I can do whatever I set my mind to	4	3	2	1
34. I am not a quitter..	4	3	2	1
35. I will take calculated chances even if I fail	4	3	2	1
36. I often blame my misfortune on others	1	2	3	4
37. I don't let obstacles get in my way.	4	3	2	1
38. I rarely blame other when bad things happen to me. . .	4	3	2	1
39. When people say "it's impossible," I usually believe them	1	2	3	4
40. I will not let others keep me from being happy	4	3	2	1

O - TOTAL = _____

(Go to the Scoring Directions on the next page)

Optimistic Outlook Scale Scoring Directions

Resilient people are able to maintain a positive outlook in life. They are able to remain hopeful about their current situation and their future possibilities, expect good things to happen from their own efforts, and retain a positive attitude even when times are challenging. Resilient people work to overcome obstacles. For each of the four sections on the previous pages, total the scores you circled. Put that total on the line marked TOTAL at the end of each section.

Then, transfer your totals to the spaces below:

H - HOPE   **TOTAL = _____**

L – LIFE OUTLOOK   **TOTAL = _____**

A - ATTITUDE   **TOTAL   = _____**

O - OVERCOMING OBSTACLES **TOTAL = _____**

Profile Interpretation

INDIVIDUAL SCALE SCORES	TOTAL SCALES SCORES	RESULT	INDICATIONS
Scores from 31 to 40	Scores from 123 to 180	High	You have developed and you use many skills and attitudes that lead to a positive outlook and a resilient personality.
Scores from 20 to 30	Scores from 79 to 122	Moderate	You have developed and you use some skills and attitudes that lead to a positive outlook and a resilient personality.
Scores from 10 to 19	Scores from 40 to 78	Low	You have not developed or used many skills and attitudes that lead to a positive outlook and a resilient personality.

For scales scored in the moderate or low range, find the descriptions on the pages that follow. Read the description and complete the exercises that are included. No matter how you scored, low, moderate or high, you will benefit from these exercises.

© 2011 WHOLE PERSON ASSOCIATES, 101 W. 2ND ST., SUITE 203, DULUTH MN 55802 • 800-247-6789

Hope

Hope can be described as a mindset consisting of a positive view of the future for yourself and others. Remaining hopeful over the course of your life is at the core of resiliency and the ability to bounce back while facing psychological threats and stress. Resilient people are able to feel spiritual and psychological peace in the throes of suffering, pain, and disaster. Hope is important in sustaining joy and happiness as you live your life. Having hope has special powers for healing and guiding you with resiliency while you attain life goals and dreams.

Respond to the following questions to identify your hope patterns:

What does the statement "Hope springs eternal" mean to you?

_____

_____

_____

_____

What in your life has caused you to stop hoping?

_____

_____

_____

_____

Where do you believe your sources of hope, or lack of hope, come from?

_____

_____

_____

_____

How has the way you were brought up affected the amount of hope you currently have?

_____

_____

_____

_____

(Continued on the next page)

Hope *(Continued)*

Where do you look for hope in your life?

_____

_____

_____

_____

What are three things you hope for?

1. _____

    _____

2. _____

    _____

3. _____

    _____

How have your hopes changed over your lifetime?

_____

_____

_____

_____

How has hope, or a lack of hope, affected decisions you have made?

_____

_____

_____

_____

What needs to happen before you have more hope in your life?

_____

_____

_____

_____

Life Outlook

Do you believe yourself to be an optimist or pessimist? Why do you believe this?

_____

_____

_____

_____

How long have you been an optimist or pessimist? What brought this world-view on?

_____

_____

_____

_____

How did your childhood affect the way you view the world?

_____

_____

_____

_____

How can you begin to view the world in an even more positive light?

_____

_____

_____

_____

Think of a time when you viewed a situation as negative, and yet, something positive came out of it?

_____

_____

_____

_____

_____

Optimistic People in my life

It is advantageous to surround yourself with people who are optimistic.

Complete the table below:

Optimistic People I Know	How They Show Their Optimism
(Ex: My friend Larry)	*(When I am upset he always tries to show me the bright side of the situation.)*

© 2011 WHOLE PERSON ASSOCIATES, 101 W. 2ND ST., SUITE 203, DULUTH MN 55802 • 800-247-6789

Pessimistic People in My Life

It is advantageous to reduce or eliminate contact with people in your life who are pessimistic. Complete the table below:

Pessimistic People I Know	How They Show Their Pessimism
(Ex: My friend Mort)	*(When I am upset he always finds more reasons for me to be upset about the situation.)*

Reconstructing My Attitude

When you find yourself getting stuck in a cycle of negative thinking, what is one method you can try to restructure your thinking from pessimistic to optimistic?

Consider the situation, as an example, of going back to school.

- When you feel yourself becoming negative, identify your negative thoughts: *"I'm not good enough," "I'm not smart enough," "Everyone will be much younger than me," "I have not been to school in such a long time."*

- Think about the accuracy of your statements. What is the proof they are accurate? When you look at them objectively, what do you learn?

- Think of positive ways to restructure these thoughts. *"If other people can go back to college so can I," "I will be more experienced than many of the other students," "It's never too late to learn," "I deserve the benefits of going back to school."*

- Take action: *"I will go to the school on Friday and pick up an application. I will complete it over the weekend and search online for information about financial aid."*

Now You Try

State a time when you had negative thoughts about a situation that kept you from following through.

_____

_____

What were your negative thoughts?

_____

_____

How accurate were they? Was there proof?

_____

_____

How could you have restructured your thinking?

_____

_____

How could you have taken action?

_____

_____

Obstacles in My Life

It is important for you to identify and confront the obstacles in your life. These obstacles could be relationships, attitudes, habits, situations, things you lack such as more education or experience. In the table below, in the left hand column, describe an obstacles and how they block you. In the right hand column, describe what you can do to overcome those obstacles.

A Life Obstacle and How It Blocks Me	What I Can Do to Overcome This Obstacle
(Ex: I don't know how to use the computer very well.)	*(I can take a class at the library.)*

Obstacles in My Work

It is also important for you to identify and confront the obstacles in your career. These obstacles could be people, attitudes, habits, situations, things you lack such as training. In the table that follows, describe the obstacles in your life in the left-hand column, and then in the right-hand column list some ways you might be able to overcome these obstacles.

Career Obstacles and How They Block Me	What I Can Do to Overcome This Obstacle
(EX: I cannot get further at my place of work because I don't have enough computer skills.)	*(I can take a class in the evenings or on weekends.)*

Overcoming Obstacles

Obstacles are present in the lives of everyone, but optimistic people continually work to find ways to overcome those obstacles.

From the completed Obstacles in My Life handout, what theme(s) do you see related to the obstacles in your life?

_____

_____

_____

_____

From the completed Obstacles in My Work handout, what theme(s) do you see related to the obstacles in your career or volunteer work?

_____

_____

_____

_____

What goals can you immediately begin working toward to help overcome your obstacles in these areas?

_____

_____

_____

_____

What risks can you take, even though you may be reluctant, to help you overcome these obstacles?

_____

_____

_____

_____

Building an Optimistic Outlook

Optimistic people look for the good qualities in other people. List the people whom you know and identify their good qualities.

People I Know	Positive Qualities
Ex: My sister Sue	*She is assertive without being aggressive. She gets what she wants and needs without hurting anyone else.*

Creating Goals

Optimistic people set small attainable goals and then reward themselves when the goals are attained.

Goals	Ways I Will Reward Myself When My Goal Is Achieved
Ex: To develop better computer skills	*When I complete my nightly computer course I will celebrate at my favorite restaurant.*

Optimism Quotations

Choose two of these quotes. How does each speak to your feelings about optimism? Or if you disagree with a quote, write about it as well.

Optimism is essential to achievement and it is also the foundation of courage and true progress. ~ **Nicholas Butler**

Too much of a good thing is wonderful. ~ **May West**

My optimism for life carried through my work. ~ **John Dyer**

One of the things I learned the hard way was that it doesn't pay to get discouraged. Keeping busy and making optimism a way of life can restore your faith in yourself.
~ **Lucille Ball**

Optimism is the faith that leads to achievement. Nothing can be done without hope and confidence. ~ **Helen Keller**

The average pencil is seven inches long, with just a half-inch eraser – in case you thought optimism was dead. ~ **Robert Brault**

_____
_____
_____
_____
_____
_____
_____
_____
_____
_____
_____
_____
_____
_____
_____
_____

My Plan

Journal about how you plan on becoming a more optimistic person.

_____

_____

_____

_____

_____

_____

_____

_____

_____

_____

_____

_____

_____

_____

_____

_____

_____

_____

Who can you share your plan with? Who can support you?

_____

_____

_____

_____

_____

_____

Benefits of Optimism

With optimistic thinking, there is a greater chance of these results:

- Rates of infectious disease, poor health, and earlier mortality diminish.

- Achievement, (including more reliability and productivity in the workplace), better chance of getting a job, and quicker advancement within an organization.

- Persistence and completion of goals in the face of obstacles.

- Recovery of any type.

- Emotional and mental health enhanced.

- People who believe in themselves and expect good things happen to them, find that life improves.

- Willingness to take calculated risks and create more positive events in life.

- Satisfaction personal relationships.

- Success in school, training programs and learning endeavors.

- Physical health and longevity improve.

Optimism . . .

- can be learned.

- helps overcome obstacles.

- assists people in problem solving situations.

- provides energy to achieve goals.

- develops strengths to persist and persevere.

- supports one when life presents challenges.

- encourages hope.

- builds confidence in the future.

***Optimism is expecting the best possible outcome
from any given situation.***

SECTION II:
Locus of Control Scale

Name_____

Date_____

Locus of Control Scale Directions

Locus of control refers to your beliefs about what causes the good or bad things that happen in your life. It is the extent to which you believe that you can control the events that affect you, in your personal and professional life.

This assessment contains 30 statements related to three important resistance resources that can help build protection against stress. Read each of the statements and decide whether or not the statement describes you. If the statement describes you, circle the number under the YES column, next to that item. If the statement does not describe you, circle the number under the NO column, next to that item.

In the following example, the circled number under YES indicates the statement is descriptive of the person completing the inventory.

	YES	NO
Others control my life	(1)	2

This is not a test and there are no right or wrong answers. Do not spend too much time thinking about your answers. Your initial response will be the most true for you. Be sure to respond to every statement.

(Turn to the next page and begin)

Locus of Control Scale

	YES	NO
Others control my life	1	2
I create my own destiny	2	1
I determine the course of my life	2	1
When I make a plan, I make it work	2	1
I am often the victim of forces I cannot understand	1	2
I trust my life to fate	1	2
Heredity determines the success of people	1	2
I believe that what is going to happen will happen	1	2
People cannot change basic behavior patterns	1	2
People can rise above their family upbringing	2	1

C - TOTAL = _____

	YES	NO
I rarely plan too far ahead	1	2
I usually reach the goals I set for myself	2	1
Luck has nothing to do with being successful	2	1
To get ahead, I must be in the right place at the right time	1	2
If I work hard enough, I can succeed	2	1
People get promoted mainly because their supervisors like them, or they know someone	1	2
I believe I can change tomorrow by what I do today	2	1
People can get their own way if they keep trying	2	1
When good things happen it's often because of hard work	2	1
With enough effort, people can get what they want	2	1

P - TOTAL = _____

(Continued on the next page)

(Locus of Control Scale continued)

	YES	NO
When I get what I want, it is because of what I did, not luck	2	1
Some people are just born lucky	1	2
I believe that wishing can make good things happen	1	2
A lucky charm works	1	2
Getting what I want has little to do with luck	2	1
I have a good luck charm that I rely on	1	2
I believe it is better to be smart than lucky	2	1
Some people get all of the lucky breaks	1	2
I make my own luck	2	1
Bad luck seems to follow me around	1	2

L = TOTAL = _____

(Go to the Scoring Directions on the next page)

Locus of Control Scale Scoring Directions

Locus of control lies on a continuum based on an internal locus of control in which you believe that you are in control of your own life, to an external locus of control in which you believe that your environment or other people control your destiny and your life.

For the sections you just completed, add the numbers that you circled in each section. Transfer the totals below. For your overall Locus of Control total, add the three scores.

C — **Control**   Total   =   _____

P — **Persistence** Total   =   _____

L — **Luck**   Total   =   _____

_____

Locus of Control   Total   =   _____

Profile Interpretation

INDIVIDUAL SCALE SCORE	TOTAL FOR ALL THREE SCALES SCORES	RESULT	INDICATIONS
Scores from 17 to 20	Scores from 51 to 60	High	High Scores indicate that you believe your behavior is guided by your own personal decisions and efforts. The following exercises will help you to continue building locus of control resources.
Scores from 14 to 16	Scores from 40 to 50	Moderate	Moderate Scores indicate that you believe your behavior is guided by a combination of your own efforts and some external circumstances. Complete the following exercises to build more of the locus of control resources that will benefit you.
Scores from 10 to 13	Scores from 30 to 39	Low	Low Scores indicate that you believe your behavior is guided by fate, luck, or other external circumstances. Complete the following exercises to build the locus of control resources that will benefit you.

The Development of Locus of Control

Locus of control develops from a combination of family, cultural influences and previous experiences. Let's examine those factors in your life.

What did your mother/female caregiver believe about the factors that lead to success or failure?

_____

_____

_____

What did your mother/female caregiver believe about luck leading to success or failure?

_____

_____

_____

What did your father/male caregiver believe about the factors that lead to success or failure?

_____

_____

_____

What did your father/male caregiver believe about luck leading to success or failure?

_____

_____

_____

As a child growing up, how were you encouraged to take responsibility for your own destiny?

_____

_____

_____

As a child growing up, how did your cultural, spiritual and/or religious beliefs affect your thoughts about your destiny?

_____

_____

_____

Contributing to My Successes

It is important to look at how you have contributed to the successes in your life.

The Success	How I Contributed to the Success
Ex: I graduated from community college.	*I studied hard, asked people for help when I needed it, worked on campus to help pay for my classes and books.*

My Disappointments

It is equally important to look at the disappointments in your life. In the table that follows, describe your disappointments and the ways you contributed to your future in a negative way.

The Disappointment	How I Contributed to My Future in a Negative Way
Ex: I dropped out of high school	*I did not go to class. I listened to my friends who said school was not important and it would be more fun to be with them.*

How can you have more of a positive impact in future situations?

_____

_____

_____

Gaining More Control over Your Daily Life

One way to have more control over what happens daily is to create a situation for yourself where good things can happen. You may need to change your patterns within your family, friendships and work.

Better Situations for Me	How This Can Help
Ex: Change my bowling league so I can go to my children's baseball games on Thursday nights.	My wife will feel supported and the children will be happy that I'm there for them.

© 2011 WHOLE PERSON ASSOCIATES, 101 W. 2ND ST., SUITE 203, DULUTH MN 55802 ▪ 800-247-6789

Action Plan

This section will help you develop an action plan to take more control of your life. You can exert more control over your life than you ever imagined.

Step 1 — My Life

Identify areas in your life where you feel dissatisfied or in a rut. Think about where you feel unfulfilled — relationships, work, family responsibilities. hopes and dreams, etc.

State one of your unfulfilled areas: (*Ex: further education*)

_____

Step 2 — Look at Your Attitude

Take a look at your attitude as it relates to the area you indentified above in Step 1. It is through your attitude that you limit yourself and remain stuck. By confronting and changing your attitude, you can empower yourself to make positive changes in your life.

Think about the negative and limiting attitudes. What might be keeping you stuck?

FAMILY BELIEFS

My family passed on these negative beliefs to me about my ability to influence my life:

(*EX: "You don't have the brains you were born with."*)

_____

_____

_____

PERSONAL LIMITATIONS AND BELIEFS

What attitudes and beliefs do you have about yourself that limit your exerting control over your situation?

Example:

- *I do not have enough life skills*
- *I will never succeed*
- *I am not as smart as other people*
- *I do not communicate very well*

Now you try. List the personal limitation and beliefs you have about yourself:

_____

_____

_____

(Continued)

(Action Plan continued)

ATTITUDES ABOUT OTHERS

You may have negative attitudes about other people in your life.

Example:

- *My peers think they are so smart*
- *My partner doesn't respect what I have to say*
- *My supervisor doesn't think I deserve a promotion*
- *My parents are to blame*

Now you try. List the negative attitudes and beliefs you have about people in your life:

_____

_____

_____

_____

_____

_____

_____

_____

Remember, it is what YOU believe about yourself, NOT what others believe about you, that can influence you in either a positive or a negative way.

Step 3 — Changing Your Attitude

In step 3, you have the opportunity to identify ways to change negative attitudes and move past the issues you identified in Step 1. These attitudes and beliefs can be overcome with a few simple techniques:

Notice when negative thoughts pop into your head, Stop that negative self-talk, challenge it and substitute more positive self-talk.

Now that you have identified negative thoughts and attitudes in Step 2, think about whether the thoughts are accurate, or not. What evidence is there for their accuracy?

In the following table, list your negative thoughts and the evidence you have for their accuracy.

(Continued)

(Action Plan continued)

Negative Attitudes	Evidence for These Attitudes
Ex: I'm not smart enough to go to college.	*Nothing, other than what my parents told me.*

(Continued)

(Action Plan continued)

Repeat your negative thoughts from the previous page in the first column and then substitute positive thoughts for those negative thoughts.

Negative Attitudes	Substitute Positive Thoughts from the First Column
(EX: I cannot get further at my place of work because I don't have enough computer skills.)	*I am smart enough to go to college. I will start with a community college where I can receive personalized assistance.*

(Continued)

(Action Plan continued)

STEP 4 — Set Goals for Change

Goals can help you regain control in your life. List several of your goals and hopes related to the area in which you feel stuck. For example:

- *I want a job where I feel more challenged*
- *I want to further my education*
- *I want to learn more about technology*
- *I want to feel smart*

List two goals related to the unfulfilled area you identified in Step 1:

Goal #1: _____

_____

Goal #2: _____

_____

Step 5 — Identify Short-term Steps — Begin Moving Toward Your Goals

These short-term steps are action-oriented activities to move you toward the general goals you identified in the last step. In the table the follows, list the short-term steps you will begin taking to reach ONE of your goals and the deadlines you set for completing each step.

Steps I Will Take for One of My Goals	Deadlines for Completing Steps
Ex: I will call my local community college and make an appointment with a counselor.	*tomorrow*
I will keep my appointment with the counselor, even if I am apprehensive!	*next week*
If I like the school I will fill out an application. If not, I'll look for another one.	*the next day*

(Continued)

(Action Plan continued)

STEP 6 — Take Action

It's time to take action by taking control of your life.

Steps I Have Completed

Steps I Am Having Trouble Completing

Why do you think you are having trouble completing some of the steps? Can you revise them to make them more doable?

_____

_____

_____

How has this process, or how will this process, help you to take greater control of the events in your life?

_____

_____

_____

To Know What I Can and Cannot Control

In life, there are certain things that you cannot control. It is important that you identify them and not waste time, emotional and physical energy, trying to change them. In the following boxes, list what you can and cannot control:

I Can Control . . .	I Cannot Control . . .
Ex: Getting to work on time every day.	*My company downsized fifty workers.*

Locus of Control Quotes

Describe what each quote means to you on the lines that follow.

Could we change our attitude, we should not only see life differently, but life itself would come to be different. ~ **Katherine Mansfield**

_____

_____

The size of your success is measured by the strength of your desire; the size of your dream, and how you handle disappointment along the way. ~ **Robert Kiyosaki**

_____

_____

No life is so hard that you can't make it easier by the way you take it. ~ **Ellen Glasgow**

_____

_____

We must accept finite disappointment but never lose infinite hope. ~ **Martin Luther King, Jr.**

_____

_____

I long to accomplish a great and noble task, but it is my chief duty to accomplish small tasks as if they were great and noble. ~ **Helen Keller**

_____

_____

I cannot always control what goes on outside. But I can always control what goes on inside. ~ **Wayne Dyer**

_____

_____

Whether you prevail or fail, endure or die, depends more on what you do to yourself than on what the world does to you. ~ **Jim Collins**

_____

_____

Your Locus of Control

Why is it so important to understand your locus of control?

What have you learned about your locus on control?

To Change Your Locus of Control . . .

- Realize that you have choices that can change most situations.

- Know that you can always change your attitude to alter how you view a situation.

- Brainstorm various courses of action.

- Monitor your "self-talk."

- Recognize what you can change.

- Know what you cannot change.

- Remember that you can learn to be more internally oriented.

Results of a Healthy Locus of Control

- Self-determination increases

- Stress management skills develop

- Achievement orientation sharpens

- Decision making skills improve

- Problem solving skills expand

- Responsibility for one's own limitations

- Self-confidence grows

- Recognition of one's personal responsibility for self-control, seeking opportunities, and investigating effects of others.

SECTION III:
Sense-of-Self Scale

Name_____

Date_____

Sense-of-Self Scale Directions

Resilient people have an excellent sense-of-self. They believe in themselves, understand themselves, and maintain confidence in their abilities. The purpose of this assessment is to help you become aware of your self-esteem, self-confidence and self-concept.

This scale contains 24 statements divided into three sections. Read each statement and decide how true the statement is for you. In the following example, the circled "2" indicates that the statement is Somewhat True for the person completing the inventory:

	True	Somewhat True	Not True
SECTION I			
I find it difficult to value myself	1	(2)	3

This is not a test and there are no right or wrong answers. Do not spend too much time thinking about your answers. Your initial response will be the most true for you. Be sure to respond to every statement.

(Turn to the next page and begin)

Sense-of-Self Scale

	True	Somewhat True	Not True
SECTION I			
I find it difficult to value myself	1	2	3
I believe I have nothing to contribute to society	1	2	3
I measure success against my own standard, not those of society	3	2	1
I worry about what others think about me	1	2	3
I appreciate my own worth and importance	3	2	1
I see other people as being better than me	1	2	3
I am as important as anyone else	3	2	1
I am able to overcome adversity and setbacks	3	2	1
I – TOTAL = _____			
SECTION II			
I live my life based on what I truly value	3	2	1
I take responsibility for my choices and actions	3	2	1
I don't like how I look	1	2	3
I am honest with myself	3	2	1
I have trouble accepting myself as I am	1	2	3
On the whole, I am satisfied with myself	3	2	1
I do not feel equipped to handle what comes my way	1	2	3
I know I have potential, but I don't know what it is	1	2	3
II – TOTAL = _____			
SECTION III			
I tend to do what is expected of me rather than what I feel is right	1	2	3
I am willing to take risks to achieve what I want	3	2	1
I admit my mistakes and learn from them	3	2	1
It is difficult for me to accept compliments	1	2	3
I handle new situations with comfort and ease	3	2	1
If something looks too difficult, I avoid it	1	2	3
I believe that if I work hard, I will succeed	3	2	1
I often feel the need to be right	1	2	3
III – TOTAL = _____			

(Go to the Scoring Directions on the next page)

Sense-of-Self Scale Scoring Directions

Add the totals for each section of the scale and then transfer those totals below.

SECTION I   Self-Esteem   TOTAL = _____

SECTION II   Self-Concept   TOTAL = _____

SECTION III   Self-Confidence   TOTAL = _____

To receive your overall Sense-of-Self total, total the three scores above.

SENSE-OF-SELF TOTAL = _____

Profile Interpretation

INDIVIDUAL SCALE SCORE	TOTAL SCALES SCORES	RESULT	INDICATIONS
Scores from 8 to 13	Scores from 24 to 40	Low	You tend to have less sense-of-self than resilient people. However, you can develop a greater sense-of-self and become more resilient.
Scores from 14 to 18	Scores from 41 to 55	Moderate	You tend to have a pretty good sense-of-self, approaching that of resilient people. However, you can develop a greater sense-of-self and become more resilient.
Scores from 19 to 24	Scores from 56 to 72	High	You tend to have a good sense-of-self, similar to that of resilient people. However, you can continue to develop a greater sense-of-self and become even more resilient.

The higher your score on this scale, the greater is your sense-of-self. In the areas in which you score in the Moderate or Low range, make an effort to continue to build your self-esteem, self-concept and self-confidence. No matter whether you scored Low, Moderate or High, the exercises and activities that follow will help you build your resiliency.

Sense-of Self

Your sense-of-self is a unique combination of your self-esteem, self-concept and self-confidence. Each of these three factors is equally important, and all three are constantly interacting to help you to determine your sense-of-self.

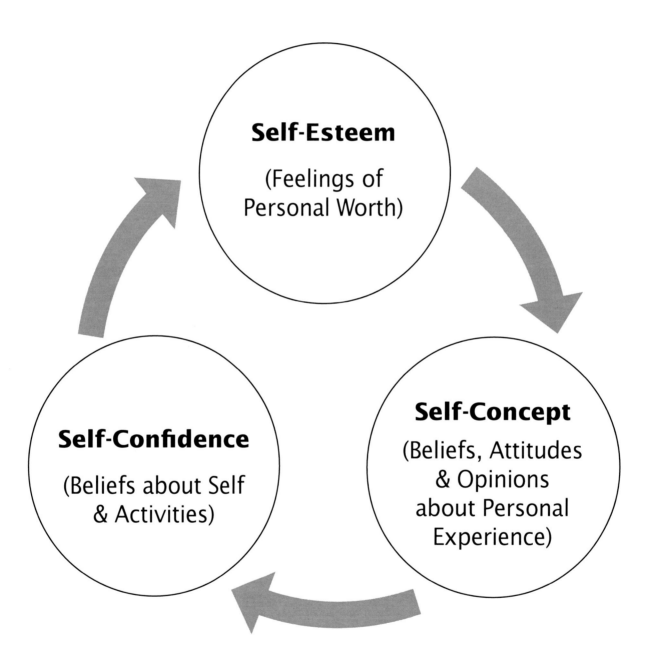

Self-Esteem

My Good Points

You can raise your self-esteem by recognizing your abilities, skills and personal qualities. In the spaces below, make a list of the characteristics you like about yourself.

My Good Points	Describe These Good Points
Abilities	*Ex: I am a great baseball left-fielder.*
Skills	*Ex: I am very organized.*
Personal Qualities	*Ex: I am extremely compassionate.*

(Continued on the next page)

(Self-Esteem continued)

What Others Like About Me

What Others Like About Me	Describe These Good Points
Abilities	*Ex: I am handy to have around.*
Skills	*Ex: I remember trivia.*
Personal Qualities	*Ex: I am supportive.*

Summarize your qualities based on the previous two tables.

_____

_____

_____

_____

_____

_____

Self-Criticisms

Sometimes we have an inner voice that tells us how wrong, bad or undeserving we are. This inner critic can keep us from feeling good about ourselves. List the characteristics you do not like about yourself, ways you show your characteristics and how you can change them.

Characteristics I Do Not Like About Myself	How I Show These Characteristics	How I Can Change them
Ex: I am not assertive enough	I do whatever someone tells me to do and ignore what I want to do.	I can say what's on my mind in an honest, open and direct way, and do what I believe to be right.

Self-Concept

Your self-concept is how you view yourself. A healthy self-concept is important in developing resiliency since the way you view yourself determines how you experience life. If your self-concept is positive, you will experience life that way. However, if your self-concept is fragile, and you are insecure, you will tend to feel overwhelmed when facing life's challenges. Your self-concept can be described as who you are and how you fit into the world. The following exercises are designed to help you develop a healthy self-concept.

Know Yourself

How are you unique?

_____

_____

_____

_____

_____

What would you like to change about yourself?

_____

_____

_____

_____

_____

In what ways are you worthwhile?

_____

_____

_____

_____

_____

(Continued on the next page)

(Self-Concept continued)

What do you accept about yourself?

_____

_____

_____

_____

_____

About what do you criticize yourself? How accurate are these criticisms?

_____

_____

_____

_____

_____

What about your appearance do you like?

_____

_____

_____

_____

_____

What about your appearance do you dislike?

_____

_____

_____

_____

_____

Self-Confidence

We are not born with self-confidence; we learn and develop self-confidence from our interactions with other people. In other words, self-confidence can be learned and unlearned. The following activities can help you develop greater self-confidence in your personal and professional lives.

Role Models

Think about the people you know who appear to have self-confidence. In the left hand column of the table below, list three people who, by your observations and by their mannerisms, could be role-models of self-confidence. These people may be dead or alive, famous people from history, or people in your life now. In the middle column, list what you think might have helped them to be self-confident and in the third column describe how they act.

Role Models	What Made Them Confident	How They Acted
Ex: Helen Keller	*Even though people told her she would be limited, she refused to believe that.*	*Instead of acting like a victim, she took responsibility for her life.*

(Continued on the next page)

(Self-confidence continued)

Comparisons

One way you can develop greater self-confidence is by not comparing yourself negatively with other people. The first step in doing so is to identify those people with whom you typically compare yourself. In the table that follows, identify the people with whom you compare yourself, how you compare yourself and something positive about yourself.

Who I Compare Myself To	How I Compare Myself To Them	What I Have Going for Me!
Ex: My best friend Jim.	I compare my salary to his.	I have a great family life – he doesn't.

(Continued on the next page)

(Self-Confidence continued)

My Successes

Remember your successes from the past. Success breeds increased sense-of-self and self-esteem. In the table that follows, draw pictures or write about your greatest successes in the various aspects of your life. Feel free to use blank sheets of paper to continue with more successes.

Success With My Family	Success in School
Success at Work	**Success in the Community**
Success in my Spare Time	**Other Successes**

(Continued on the next page)

(Self-Confidence continued)

Taking Calculated Risks

Self-confident people are able to take careful and calculated risks that bring them greater success, happiness and achievement.

What personal risks have you taken in the past that have led to success for you?

_____

_____

_____

_____

What personal risks have you not taken in the past that probably would have led to greater self-confidence?

_____

_____

_____

_____

What job or volunteer risks have you taken in the past that have led to success for you?

_____

_____

_____

_____

What job or volunteer risks have you not taken in the past that probably would have led to greater self-confidence?

_____

_____

_____

_____

(Continued) on the next page

(Self-Confidence continued)

Taking Calculated Risks

In the following table write about risks that you might take in the future that can lead to greater success, happiness and achievement.

A Risk I Can Take	How It Can Lead to Success
Ex: Accept a volunteer position at the food bank.	*I'll feel good about myself by helping people instead of watching TV and I might meet people who can help me find a job in the future.*

Sense-of-Self Quotations

Place a check mark by the quote(s) that you feel might inspire you to have greater sense –of-self. You can cut the quotes out and post them by your computer, on your refrigerator or you can tuck them into your wallet. At the bottom of the page, write about why the quote(s) spoke to you.

No one can make you feel inferior without your consent. ~ **Eleanor Roosevelt**

Someone's opinion of you does not have to become your reality. ~ **Les Brown**

It took me a long time not to judge myself through someone else's eyes. ~ **Sally Field**

You were not born a winner, and you were not born a loser. You are what you make yourself to be. ~ **Lou Holtz**

Self-trust is the first secret of success. ~ **Ralph Waldo Emerson**

Aerodynamically the bumblebee shouldn't be able to fly, but the bumblebee doesn't know that so it goes on flying anyway. ~ **Mary Kay Ash**

You have within you right now, everything you need to deal with whatever the world can throw at you. ~ **Brian Tracy**

_____

_____

_____

_____

_____

_____

_____

_____

_____

My Characteristics

What positive qualities did you learn that you possess? How will you foster those qualities?

_____

_____

_____

_____

_____

_____

_____

_____

_____

_____

_____

What personal negative characteristics did you learn? How will you change those characteristics?

_____

_____

_____

_____

_____

_____

_____

_____

_____

_____

_____

_____

_____

Sense-of-Self and Resilience

How can a greater sense-of-self help you to be more resilient?

_____

_____

_____

_____

_____

_____

_____

_____

_____

_____

_____

_____

_____

_____

_____

_____

_____

_____

_____

_____

_____

_____

_____

_____

_____

_____

_____

_____

The Sense-of-Self Circle

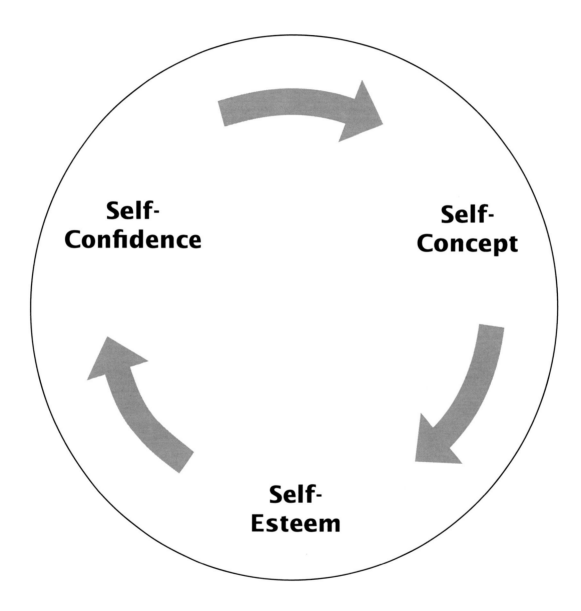

Facts about Sense-of-Self

- A sense-of-self is learned.

- Perceived successes and failures impact one's sense-of-self.

- People see themselves differently from the ways others perceive them.

- Sense-of-self is relatively stable but can be altered.

- People behave in ways consistent with their sense-of-self.

- Faulty thinking patterns can create a negative sense-of-self.

Sense-of-self consists of three parts:
>Self-esteem
>Self-concept
>Self-confidence

Self-criticism can negatively effect one's sense-of-self.

SECTION IV:
Ability to Bounce Back Scale

Name_____

Date_____

Ability to Bounce Back Scale Directions

People who are able to bounce back from a difficult situation or crisis, tend to feel that what happens in their lives is a result of their own actions and within their control. On the other hand, people who act and believe that they are victims, tend to feel life has not treated them fairly. They feel everyone and everything else is to blame for what happens in their lives. This scale helps to identify your current mind-set. Read each statement carefully and circle the number of the response that describes you best.

	TRUE	USUALLY	RARELY	NOT TRUE
1. I have trouble taking risks	1	2	③	4

In the above example, the circled 3 indicates that the responder sometimes has trouble taking risks.

This is not a test and there are no right or wrong answers. Do not spend too much time thinking about your answers. Your initial response will be the most true for you. Be sure to respond to every statement.

(Turn to the next page and begin)

Ability to Bounce Back Scale

	TRUE	USUALLY	RARELY	NOT TRUE
1. I have trouble taking risks	1	2	3	4
2. I often ask why terrible things keep happening to me	1	2	3	4
3. I embrace the unknown rather than run from it	4	3	2	1
4. I tend to be judgmental of others	1	2	3	4
5. I use humor to help me through tough times	4	3	2	1
6. I can find solutions to problems in times of trouble	4	3	2	1
7. I accept differences in other people	4	3	2	1
8. I do not perform well under pressure	1	2	3	4
9. I am calm and focused under pressure	4	3	2	1
10. I am not very flexible or adaptable	1	2	3	4
11. I want to leave the world better than I found it	4	3	2	1
12. I worry about what others say about me	1	2	3	4
13. I do not rely on my intuition very much	1	2	3	4
14. I can be playful and childlike when it is appropriate	4	3	2	1
15. I am not very spontaneous	1	2	3	4
16. I enjoy learning things about myself	4	3	2	1
17. I care about the well-being of others	4	3	2	1
18. I have a hard time motivating myself	1	2	3	4
19. I believe awful things are always going to happen to me	1	2	3	4
20. I am committed to survival regardless of my situation	4	3	2	1
21. I am able to make light of myself even in difficult situations	4	3	2	1
22. I worry about mistakes I have made in the past	1	2	3	4
23. I continue on even if there is conflicting information and uncertainty	4	3	2	1
24. I have a lot of regrets that I dwell on	1	2	3	4
25. I tackle my problems and find solutions	4	3	2	1
26. I never give up on tasks until they are completed	4	3	2	1
27. I sometimes feel like I am a victim	1	2	3	4
28. I am able to learn from my mistakes	4	3	2	1
29. I turn stressful situations into personal challenges	4	3	2	1
30. I often worry about looking foolish	1	2	3	4

TOTAL = _____

(Go to the Scoring Directions on the next page)

Ability to Bounce Back Scale
Scoring Directions

The scale you just completed is designed to help you explore whether your mind-set tends to allow you to bounce back from difficult situations or tends to promote your mind-set of being a victim. For each of the items on the previous pages, total the scores you circled. Add your circled numbers and put that total on the line marked TOTAL at the end of the section and then transfer that number below.

Total _____ **Ability to Bounce Back**

Profile Interpretation

TOTAL SCALE SCORE	RESULT	INDICATIONS
Scores from 91 to 120	High	You tend to have a bounce-back mentality. You have control over what happens in your life and believe that good things are going to happen to you. These exercises will help you to develop even more of a bounce-back mentality.
Scores from 60 to 90	Moderate	You tend to have a mix of the bounce-back and victim mentality. These exercises will help you to develop additional beliefs to support a bounce-back mentality.
Scores from 30 to 59	Low	You tend to have more of a victim mentality and it seems that you do not believe that you have control over what happens in your life or that good things are going to happen to you. These exercises will help you to begin to develop a bounce-back mentality.

Overcoming a Victim Mentality

A victim mentality is a self-defeating attitude with self-limiting thoughts about yourself that restrict you from reaching your full potential. A victim mentality is a feeling that one cannot make changes in one's life, and that one is living the life of a victim. Following are some activities and exercises to help you develop a bounce-back mentality.

People who have developed a victim mentality have often had many unfortunate circumstances in their past, leading to a negative, fatalistic attitude. What unfortunate circumstances have you experienced in the past? Identify these circumstances and how they affected you emotionally.

Negative Things That Occurred	How They Affected Me
Ex: My father lost his job of 15 years and was without one for quite a while.	*I was constantly worrying about our not having enough food to eat or getting new clothes. I was probably disagreeable to my friends and family.*

Overcoming Negative Messages

To overcome feeling like a victim, you need to release yourself from those negative messages you receive now or received in the past, that tell you to behave or think in a certain way. Think about the people in your life giving you negative messages about how to think, act or feel. List those people from your life, such as teachers, parents, friends, siblings, relatives, religious leaders, etc., and the things they tell you. Then, in the last column, reverse the negative message to make it more positive.

People From My Life	Things They Say	How Have You, or Can You, Reverse This Message?
Ex: My Aunt Hilda	*You're so argumentative. You'll never stay in a relationship.*	*I am assertive and this is a plus for me in my relationships with assertive people.*

Invest in Yourself

By investing in yourself, you can make yourself more valuable in a variety of roles. Think about ways that you can feel empowered in situations you might encounter. List the ways that you can make yourself more valuable.

Situations	How I Can Invest in Myself
Ex: Work	*If I get additional training in web design I can make myself even more valuable.*
Work	
Education	
Community	
Health & Wellness	
Family	
Other	

© 2011 WHOLE PERSON ASSOCIATES, 101 W. 2ND ST., SUITE 203, DULUTH MN 55802 ▪ 800-247-6789

Take More Responsibility

People with a bounce-back mentality take responsibility for what happens in their lives. Instead of blaming others for the bad things that happen, they are empowered by taking total responsibility for what happens to them. List the ways you can take more responsibility for your life.

Situations	How I Can Take More Responsibility
Ex: Work	*I will use my time more effectively at work to get more done.*
Work	
Education	
Community	
Health & Wellness	
Family	
Other	

Learn From Your Experiences

People with a bounce-back mentality are able to look at their experiences and find ways to use them to be more effective, capable and employable. List some of the negative things that have happened to you and what you can learn from these situations.

Negative Things in My Life	What I Can Learn
Ex: I was laid off from work.	I don't know enough about computers. I need to get additional training to become more employable.

Excuses

People with a bounce-back mentality do not blame or use excuses to explain their behavior or the behavior of others.

What kind of things have you blamed on your circumstances?

(Ex: My inability to find the perfect partner.)

_____

_____

_____

_____

_____

What excuses do you use?

(Ex: I can't afford it, I don't deserve it, etc.)

_____

_____

_____

_____

How do excuses keep you from taking healthy risks?

(Ex: Lack of money to impress someone, so why even try?)

_____

_____

_____

_____

How do excuses keep you from taking responsibility?

(Ex: I rarely call people back after a date because I'm sure they will not go out with me again!)

_____

_____

_____

_____

Staying in the Present vs. Dwelling on the Past

People with a bounce-back mentality do not dwell on the past or let the past influence their choices in the present or their vision for the future. Describe some influences from your past and how they may have prevented you from being more successful.

Influences from the Past	How These Influences Might Have Prevented Me from Being Successful
Ex: My father passed away when I was seven years old and I grew up in a single-parent home.	*My mom did a great job in raising me, but I missed out on a father-figure in my life. I feel like I did not have the same good experiences as some of my friends.*

Prepare for the Future

People with a bounce-back mentality live in the present, but are aware of ways they can influence their future. Describe what you can do in the future to influence your life in a positive way and how it will empower you.

Ways I Will Influence My Future	How It Will Empower Me
Ex: I will take an anger management class.	*I will be able to handle difficult situations in a more assertive and reasonable way.*

(Continued on the next page)

(Prepare for the Future continued)

What about the future is worrisome?

_____

_____

_____

_____

What can you continue to do to make your life better?

_____

_____

_____

_____

How can you let go of negative things that have happened to you?

_____

_____

_____

_____

What fears do you have about taking healthy risks?

_____

_____

_____

_____

What situations could you change by exerting a little more effort?

_____

_____

_____

_____

Get What You Deserve

People with a bounce-back mentality are not afraid to seek out and get what they feel they deserve. What are the things in your life that you feel you deserve?

Situations	Things I Deserve
Ex: Community	*I deserve a safer, crime-free neighborhood. I'll join a citizen's group to assist in keeping our area safe.*
Community	
Education	
Work	
Health & Wellness	
Family	
Other	

Focus and Commitment

People with a bounce-back mentality have focused attention and a commitment to life within which personal experiences can be interpreted with meaning and hope, even when life seems very challenging.

What is one thing (person, project, faith, etc.) to which you are committed in life?

_____

_____

_____

_____

How do you focus your attention on it?

_____

_____

_____

_____

What is the result of your focused attention (hope for the future, sense of purpose, etc.)

_____

_____

_____

_____

How will you maintain your focus and commitment to it?

_____

_____

_____

_____

Bounce-Back Quotations

Read and think about the following quotes. Pick your favorite and describe how it applies to your past life, your current life, and how you want to live in the future. Write in the spaces provided below the quotes.

Above all, be the heroine of your life, not the victim. ~ **Nora Ephron**

Self-pity is easily the most destructive of the nonpharmaceutical narcotics; it is addictive, gives momentary pleasure and separates the victim from reality. ~ **John W. Gardner**

No matter how far life pushes you down, no matter how much you hurt, you can always bounce back. ~ **Sheryl Swoopes**

When you realize the value of all life, you dwell less on what is past and concentrate more on the preservation of the future. ~ **Dian Fossey**

You build on failure. You use it as a stepping stone. Close the door on the past. You don't try to forget the mistakes, but you don't dwell on it. You don't let it have any of your energy, or any of your time, or any of your space. ~ **Johnny Cash**

Past _____

_____

_____

_____

Current _____

_____

_____

_____

Future _____

_____

_____

_____

I Learned . . .

What will you do now to develop more of a bounce-back mentality?

_____

_____

_____

_____

_____

_____

_____

_____

_____

_____

_____

_____

_____

From the activities in this chapter, what did you learn most about yourself?

_____

_____

_____

_____

_____

_____

_____

_____

_____

_____

_____

_____

_____

Handling it Differently

What are some situations that you wish you had handled differently?

_____

_____

_____

_____

_____

_____

_____

_____

_____

_____

_____

_____

In retrospect, how would you handle those situations now?

_____

_____

_____

_____

_____

_____

_____

_____

_____

_____

_____

_____

Ways to Develop
a Bounce-Back Mentality

Here's what I can do . . .

- Find new, more positive friends.

- Prepare for the future.

- Laugh and find humor in my day.

- Do not label myself or allow myself to be labeled

- Remind myself frequently of my positive attributes.

- Stay in the present without dwelling in the past.

- Overcome negative messages.

- Invest in myself.

- Take more responsibility for my own actions.

- Learn from my experiences.

- Be sure that the negative influences of the past do not contribute to my future.

- Refrain from making excuses or blaming.

- Be certain that I am, or become, the person I want to be.

Reasons People Maintain a Victim Mentality

Awareness of the benefits people derive from being a victim can help you to decide that you do not wish to be a victim, and that you will choose to take a different path.

Victims

- Victims get attention from others who want to help them.

- Victims don't have to take healthy risks, only to be rejected.

- Victims don't have to take responsibility for their life.

- Victims don't have to be responsible for the decisions they make.

- Victims enjoy the self-pity
  .

- Victims have a (false) sense of love and acceptance.

- Victims feel entitled to sympathy and kindness.

- Victims are treated kinder because of their suffering.

SECTION V:
Change Management Scale

Name_____

Date_____

Change Management Scale

We all experience changes in our lives, yet we all feel and react differently about our lives and ourselves, with varying degrees of success. Resilient people are able to look at change as an opportunity. They control their negative emotions about change and influence the outcome of the change.

Whether changes you are or have experienced is related to your career, a divorce, losing a loved one, moving your residence, starting a new relationship, returning to school, or any other type of lifestyle change, use this scale to help you examine how effectively you deal with these change when they occur.

The Change Management Scale contains 32 statements related to how you deal with change. Read each of the statements and decide whether or not the statement describes you. If the statement is true, circle the number next to that item under the TRUE column. If the statement is false, circle the number next to that item under the FALSE column.

In the following example, the circled number under FALSE indicates the statement is not true of the person completing the inventory.

Identify a change that is happening or has happened in your life.

_____

	TRUE	FALSE
When in the midst of this change, I . . .		
view it as a chance to learn something new	2	(1)

This is not a test and there are no right or wrong answers. Do not spend too much time thinking about your answers. Your initial response will likely be the most true for you. Be sure to respond to every statement.

(Turn to the next page and begin)

Change Management Scale

Identify a change that is happening or has happened in your life.

	TRUE	FALSE
When in the midst of this change, I . . .		
view it as a chance to learn something new	2	1
believe change can be to my advantage	2	1
see it as potentially scary	1	2
see it as a step further away from my goals	1	2
get excited about new opportunities	2	1
view it as a loss of power	1	2
view it as a way to be in charge of my life	2	1
hesitate to take chances	2	1

O – TOTAL = _____

	TRUE	FALSE
When in the midst of this change, I . . .		
view it in a stressful way	2	1
feel out of control and don't like it	1	2
feel shocked at first, but then move on	2	1
feel like my world has been crushed	1	2
reach out to my family and friends	2	1
struggle to remain positive	1	2
refrain from angry and/or becoming upset	2	1
tend to feel like a victim	1	2

F – TOTAL = _____

(Continued on the next page)

(Change Management Scale continued)

	TRUE	FALSE

When in the midst of this change, I . . .

	TRUE	FALSE
believe I can influence the change process	2	1
cannot control my emotional responses	1	2
work on improving my situation	2	1
seek out others who have been in similar situations	2	1
view it as a potential opportunity	2	1
see only the negatives in the situation	1	2
look for options and potential	2	1
focus on what I cannot control rather than what I can control	1	2

C– TOTAL = _____

When in the midst of this change, I . . .

	TRUE	FALSE
worry about things I can do nothing about	1	2
look at the big picture	2	1
am open to going in a new direction	2	1
feel powerless and get stuck	1	2
fear doing things and looking foolish	1	2
lose my sense-of-self	1	2
am willing and/or eager to ask for help	2	1
reach out to my support system	2	1

I – TOTAL = _____

(Go to the Scoring Directions on the next page)

Change Management Scale
Scoring Directions

This scale is designed to identify how resiliently you look at change in your personal and professional life. Total the numbers you circled for the statements, marked O, F, C and I and write the scores in each of the four sections of the scales.

Then, record those totals below.

O – Opportunity Total = _____

F – Feelings Total = _____

C – Control Total = _____

I – Influence Total = _____

_____

Total of all Scales = _____

Profile Interpretation

INDIVIDUAL SCALE SCORE	TOTAL SCALES SCORES	RESULT	INDICATIONS
Scores from 14 to 16	Scores from 54 to 64	High	A high score indicates you are able to manage the changes in your life well. Developing more effective change-management skills will make you even more resilient in the future.
Scores from 11 to 13	Scores from 43 to 53	Moderate	A moderate score indicates you are able to somewhat manage the changes in your life. Developing some additional change-management skills will help you deal effectively with current and future changes.
Scores from 8 to 10	Scores from 32 to 42	Low	A low score indicates you are not yet able to effectively manage the changes in your life. Use the following exercises to develop effective change-management skills and to assist you with current and future changes.

Change Management Scale Descriptions

Read the descriptions below and complete the exercises included in this chapter. Whether you scored, low, moderate or high, you will benefit from these exercises.

OPPORTUNITY – People scoring high on the Opportunity Scale are able to deal with change by looking at the positive aspects of changes in their life. They view each change as an opportunity rather than a setback. They are able to look at change as a chance to improve their life.

FEELINGS – People scoring high on the Feelings Scale remain positive, do not get angry and do not blame others for their situation. They are able to deal effectively with the stress associated with change and do everything in their power to act like a winner, not a victim, or ask "Why me?"

CONTROL – People scoring high on the Control Scale are able to feel in control, even if they are in the throes of change. They look for the opportunities and options available to them and see change as an opportunity to actually improve their current situation.

INFLUENCE – People scoring high on the Influence Scale are open to new experiences brought on by the change in their lives, and avoid getting stuck by refusing to worry about things they cannot control. They use their strong sense-of-self to get them through challenging situations.

Exploring Change

What are some of the biggest changes that you have seen in your family and how have these changes affected you?

_____

_____

_____

What are some of the biggest changes that you have seen in your workplace and how have these changes affected you?

_____

_____

_____

What are some of the biggest changes that you have seen in society and how have these changes affected you?

_____

_____

_____

What are some of the biggest changes that you have seen in your community and how have these changes affected you?

_____

_____

_____

What are some of the biggest changes that you have seen in other people and how have these changes affected you?

_____

_____

_____

When Change Occurs

There are changes that can affect every aspect of your life.
Identify a change that is happening or has happened in your life.

_____

Think about how you reacted to the change.

How did you feel?

_____

_____

_____

How did that change affect what you think about yourself?

_____

_____

_____

What was your initial reaction?

_____

_____

_____

How did it affect your thinking? (difficulty concentrating, forgetfulness, etc.)

_____

_____

_____

How did it affect your interactions with people?

_____

_____

_____

How did it affect you and your stress-level?

_____

_____

_____

Changes in Your Life

Identify a change that is happening or has happened in your life and respond to these questions:

_____

Opportunities

The way you view the change can be important in how well you are able to manage it.

How can you best cope with the change?

_____

_____

_____

How can you view the situation more positively?

_____

_____

_____

What can you learn from this situation?

_____

_____

_____

What new opportunities does the situation present?

_____

_____

_____

What types of risks will the change require you to take?

_____

_____

_____

My Strengths and Skills/Abilities

Identify your personal strengths and skills/abilities that you can rely on during a time of change.

Strengths	Skills/Abilities
(Ex: I am persistent, I am outgoing, etc.)	*(I am good at math, computers, etc.)*

Feelings

It is important to effectively manage your feelings during a time of change. Identify a change that is happening or has happened in your life.

_____

How did the change feel when it happened?

_____

_____

_____

_____

_____

_____

How do you feel now?

_____

_____

_____

_____

_____

_____

In the future, how can you control your emotional responses to change more effectively?

_____

_____

_____

_____

_____

_____

Acknowledging Feelings

It is helpful to acknowledge your feelings as you continue to face changes in your life. You may experience a variety of feelings that will need to be explored and expressed. The following guide may help you.

Identify a change that is happening or has happened in your life.

_____

Denial – What feelings have you experienced at this stage? (*"Is this really happening to me?"*)

_____

_____

_____

_____

Bargaining – What feelings have you experienced at this stage? (*"If I could do it again . . ."*)

_____

_____

_____

_____

Anger – What feelings have you experienced at this stage? (*"I hate Jim for doing this!"*)

_____

_____

_____

_____

Sadness/Depression – What feelings have you experiencing at this stage? (*"I give up."*)

_____

_____

_____

_____

Regaining Control

It helps to become more aware of what you have control over and what is not within your control, as you work through the change that you are experiencing. Think about how you can gain greater control in these same situations.

Identify a change that is happening or has happened in your life.

_____

List the things that you can control and cannot control about this situation.

Things I Cannot Control	Things I Can Control
(Ex: I cannot control that my partner broke up with me.)	*(I can decide to move forward and go on with my life in a positive way.)*

Support

It might be helpful for you to talk with other people who have been in a similar situation to yours.

Identify some other people who are, or could be, a support system for you.

_____

_____

_____

_____

Based on the change in your life, what opportunities might now present themselves to you?

_____

_____

_____

_____

Are you ready to be open to those opportunities?

_____

_____

_____

_____

Are there any silver linings or positives that you can take from the change?

_____

_____

_____

_____

There may be support groups that would be perfect for you. Look for one in your community by checking the internet or calling your county, city or social service agency.

Influence

Any type of change, positive or negative, can dramatically influence your personal and professional life. Identify a change that is happening or has happened in your life.

_____

Think about this change and how it will probably influence your life.

Describe three different aspects (positive or negative) in your life.

1. _____

2. _____

3. _____

How will your life be the same?

1. _____

2. _____

3. _____

How will your life be different?

1. _____

2. _____

3. _____

What, if any, negative changes might happen?

1. _____

2. _____

3. _____

What, if any, positive changes might happen?

1. _____

2. _____

3. _____

Quotations about Change

Our only security is our ability to change. ~ **John Lilly**

Change always comes bearing gifts. ~ **Price Pritchett**

If you don't like something change it: if you can't change it, change the way you think about it.
~ **Mary Engelbreit**

Change is the law of life. And those who look only to the past or present are certain to miss the future. ~ **John F. Kennedy**

Growth itself contains the germ of happiness. ~ **Pearl S. Buck**

Although the connections are not always obvious, personal change is inseparable from social and political change. ~ **Harriet Lerner**

Check your favorite and write about it.

_____

_____

_____

_____

_____

_____

_____

_____

_____

_____

_____

Managing Change Effectively

How can change provide you with opportunities?

_____

_____

_____

_____

_____

_____

_____

_____

_____

_____

_____

_____

What can you do to manage your feelings during a change?

_____

_____

_____

_____

_____

_____

_____

_____

_____

_____

_____

_____

_____

_____

(Continued on the next page)

(Managing Change Effectively continued)

How can you gain control of your life during times of change?

_____

_____

_____

_____

_____

_____

_____

_____

_____

_____

_____

_____

_____

How can you influence change when it does occur?

_____

_____

_____

_____

_____

_____

_____

_____

_____

_____

_____

_____

_____

Change can be . . .

- interesting

- a chance to learn something new

- a way to empower you

- the key to put you in charge of your life

- the discovery of hidden opportunities

- the impetus to get you unstuck

- the way to push you closer to your goals

Managing Stress During a Change

- Maintain a healthy diet

- Get enough sleep

- Walk or exercise daily

- Schedule fun things to do

- Find reasons to laugh

- Manage your time well

- Limit use of substances, caffeine and unhealthy foods

- Meditate or find quiet time daily

- Talk with supportive friends and family

wholeperson

Whole Person Associates is the leading publisher
of training resources for professionals who empower
people to create and maintain healthy lifestyles.
Our creative resources will help you work effectively with
your clients in the areas of stress management,
wellness promotion, mental health and life skills.

Please visit us at our web site: **www.wholeperson.com**.
You can check out our entire line of products,
place an order, request our print catalog, and
sign up for our monthly special notifications.

Whole Person Associates
800-247-6789